CHECK OUT WHAT'S INSIDE!

©MGA

Published 2019. Little Brother Books Ltd, Ground Floor, 23 Southernhay East, Exeter, Devon, EX1 1QL

Printed in Poland

books@littlebrotherbooks.co.uk   www.littlebrotherbooks.co.uk

The Little Brother Books trademark, email, website addresses are the sole and exclusive properties of Little Brother Books Limited.

lolsurprise.com I mgae.com

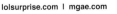

©MGA

WELCOME TO THE WORLD OF L.O.L.

ARE YOU READY TO ROCK... L.O.L. STYLE?

BRING THE BLING!

Court Champ is ready for a fierce fashion show, but where's Cherry? Help Court Champ find her before the show starts.

START

FINISH

ANSWER ON PAGE 76

If you love Boss Queen, It Baby and Cozy Babe, there's a whole bunch of fierce fun in store for you! The L.O.L. dolls want you to channel your positive vibes and get down with their cool puzzles, stories and creativity.

THE WORLD OF L.O.L. AWAITS!

GO TEAM 01 GLITTER

FASHION FEELS

Give these L.O.L. call outs a dash of sass... use glitter pens to finish them off.

Squad Goals

WHO RUNS THE WORLD? BABIES

WALKIES!

GATHER YOUR SQUAD AND UNBOX
YOUR NEXT L.O.L SURPRISE CHALLENGE!

> STRAIGHT OUTTA DAY CARE.

> Draw lines to match the club member to their pet. There's only one match in each bubble!

> PURR-FECTION.

Kitty Queen

Dollmation

M.C. Swag

GOOD BOY!

Miss Baby

Kitty Kitty

> LOOKIN' GOOD, FELINE GOOD!

> I'M ROCK ROYALTY!

> YOU BETTA WERK!

Splash Meow-Maid

Cheeky Babe

Boss Queen

> I'M BAD TO THE BONE.

Ruff Rocker

Grunge Grrrl

TREAT TIME!

> WHAT'S YOUR SIGN?

Cosmic Queen

Cheeky Hedgehog

> CHOCOLATE MILK. SHAKEN, NOT STIRRED.

Black Tie

> CODENAME: P.U.

Black Stripe

> BORN THIS WAY!

Diva

FETCH!

ANSWERS ON PAGE 76

MATCH!

DISCOVER YOUR TOGETHER 4 EVA CLUB MATCH!

BFFS 4EVA

START

Do you like to wear shades at all times?

YES → Is being glam your goal?

NO → Are leggings and big boots so you?

Is being glam your goal?
- YES → Would you totally wear a tiara?
- NO → Can you tell what people are thinking?

Are leggings and big boots so you?
- NO → Can you tell what people are thinking?
- YES → Do you love to rock out?

Would you totally wear a tiara?
- YES → Is wearing black where it's at?
- NO → Are you totally in tune with all things space?

Can you tell what people are thinking?
- YES → Are you totally in tune with all things space?
- NO → Would you love to play an instrument?

Do you love to rock out?
- YES → Would you love to play an instrument?

Is wearing black where it's at?
- YES → You're ultra cool, just like It Baby!
- NO → Are you totally in tune with all things space?

Are you totally in tune with all things space?
- YES → You're one dreamy doll, just like Cosmic Queen.

Would you love to play an instrument?
- NO → You're one dreamy doll, just like Cosmic Queen.
- YES → You're so twinning with Grunge Grrrl. You could rock out together!

You're ultra cool, just like It Baby!

You're one dreamy doll, just like Cosmic Queen.

You're so twinning with Grunge Grrrl. You could rock out together!

MISS SKUNK

MISS PUNK

©MGA

CHILLS 'N' THRILLS!

BLING ICE SK8ER AND POSH ARE HANGING ON A N-ICE DAY OUT!

Can you spot the six differences between these two scenes? Colour a coffee cup each time you spot one.

ANSWERS ON PAGE 76

10

©MGA

SNOW STYLIN'

Brrr B.B. wants to add some L.O.L. sass to her outfit! Design some earrings and a pendant for her.

YOU'VE BEEN PRANKED!

Can you see which L.O.L.s have been snowballed? Draw lines to match the names with the characters.

Snow Angel

Cozy Babe

Snow Bunny

RU GAME?

ARE YOU AN L.O.L. WORD WHIZZ?
GIVE THESE CLUB PUZZLES A WHIRL!

DO YOU WANNA BE MY BFF?

WORD UP

Search for the L.O.L. club names in the grid, and discover the club that's not included.

```
K M E F P C P T N N
G L I T T E R A T I
P F A T E H R Z N A
Q R R K N V T N G T
S O E M G P B Y H H
T C T I L O L N W L
K K R A E P A T D E
K Q O U E S R R O T
A A G L A M A I T I
A S F R J O X P X C
```

Glitterati ◯

Art ◯

Glee ◯

Rock ◯

Retro ◯

Pop ◯

Cosplay ◯

Athletic ◯

Glam ◯

ANSWERS ON PAGE 76

SOOO CREATIVE

I <3 U WITH ALL MY ART!

Which Art Club name isn't in the word wheel?

TICK THE MISSING NAME

- Pop Heart ◯
- Splatters ◯
- Shapes ◯
- Perfect Shapes ◯
- Scribbles ◯
- Eau De Splatters ◯

THE A TEAM

The L.O.L. coach has muddled up the starting team list. Rearrange the letters to discover which Athletic Club members have made the team!

TICK THE MEMBERS THAT MADE THE TEAM

OPOSH

KKCIS

WODNHCUOT

KIPES

- Hoops ◯
- Sprints ◯
- Kicks ◯
- Spike ◯
- Touchdown ◯
- Surfer Babe ◯
- Roller Sk8er ◯

13

WHO'S YOUR GLAM CLUB BFF?

ARE YOU MORE MISS BABY OR
ROYAL HIGH-NEY? LET'S FIND OUT!

1 DESCRIBE YOUR PERSONALITY:

I'm always in the
middle of any fun ⚪

Everyone wants
to know me ⚪

I'm sweet and everyone
loves to hang out with me ⚪

MISS BABY

2 WHAT'S YOUR FAVOURITE THING
TO DO WHEN YOU'RE OUT?

Take a selfie at every opportunity ⚪

Act like everyone's watching
- because they are! ⚪

Do what you can to take centre stage -
every moment is a show stopping one ⚪

3 PICK AN ACCESSORY:

Cool shades ⚪

Colour-popping shawl ⚪

Blinging tiara ⚪

4 CHOOSE A COLOUR:

Red ⚪

Pink ⚪

Blue ⚪

5 FINALLY, CHOOSE A HAIRSTYLE:

Sophisticated bob ⚪

Kiss curls ⚪

Up do ⚪

Count up your ticks and let's see which L.O.L you're most like!

ACT LIKE YOU ALREADY GOT THE PART.

MOSTLY RED

You love to be the centre of attention, and your fans love to lavish praise and adoration on you. Just like Leading Baby!

MOSTLY PINK

LET EVERYONE EAT CAKE.

Like Royal High-Ney, you have bucket loads of confidence and charm. Work it!

MOSTLY BLUE

TIARAS ARE NOT OPTIONAL.

Miss Baby was born to perform and so were you! You sparkle like a star!

GO WITH DA FLOW!

TIME TO UNLEASH THE ROCK!
TAKE A SPIN, THEN GO FOR IT!

1 Trace or photocopy the spinner on the opposite page or carefully remove the page.

2 Stick the page to card and then carefully cut out the spinner.

3 Take your pencil, and carefully pierce the middle of the spinner. Poke the pencil through the middle, with the pencil point facing downwards.

4 Your spinner game is ready. Take it in turns to spin with a friend. The spinner should land on an L.O.L challenge – take it and rock out!

16

YOU'LL NEED

SCISSORS
THIN CARD
GLUE
PENCIL

SCISSOR WARNING!

Invent a new dance move

Make up a song

Pretend to play the drums. Really go for it!

Everyone must sing together for ten seconds

Play air guitar for 30 seconds

Mess up your hair to look like a rock god

ROCK

BORN TO ROCK

FINISH ACTIVITY ON PAGE 18 BEFORE CUTTING OUT!

17

©MGA

I'LL PENCIL YOU IN!

MAKE LIKE HEARTBREAKER AND GET YOUR YEAR AHEAD OFF TO A PUMPING START!

Fill in your hopes for 2020 below. Then check back later in the year to see if you achieved them!

MY BIGGEST DREAM IS...

I'LL HAVE TOTALLY SUCCEEDED WHEN...

©MGA

MY CHALLENGES ARE...

I CAN'T WAIT FOR...

I'LL SHARE MY SPECIAL MOMENTS WITH...

If you enjoy scrapbooking, why not try keeping a diary? You only need to write a few lines every day, and you'll love looking back on it in years to come!

YOU'VE BEEN PUNKED!

UNLEASH YOUR INNER REBEL AND GO CRAZY WITH COLOUR!

Join the dots to reunite Miss Punk with Miss Skunk, then give the page a rockin' makeover!

BFFS 4EVA

MISS SKUNK

MISS PUNK

LET'S ROCK

GET YOUR L.O.L. SHOUT OUT!

WHICH CATCHPHRASE SUITS YOU BEST?

Gaze at the words below for ten seconds, then circle five words that jump out at you.

SPOTLIGHT

KIND

CLEVER

ACHIEVE   STAR

FASHION

GLAMOUR

FAMOUS   HELPFUL

SASS

POPULAR

SPARKLE

LEADER   TEAMWORK

AWESOME

Now count up your words and discover your L.O.L. motto.

MOSTLY PINK

"Glitter makes everything better" is your mantra, just like sparkly Glitter Queen!

MOSTLY BLUE

You're a classroom queen, just like Teacher's Pet. You're always on top, and your motto is "I get A's for being awesome!".

MOSTLY PURPLE

Woah, you're a show-stopping sweetie and you're "Always on pointe", just like the famous Center Stage!

21

©MGA

THE B.B. AWARDS!

JOIN THE L.O.L. DOLLS FOR A NIGHT ON THE PINK CARPET!

1

PUPARAZZI ALERT! The L.O.L.s are walking the pink carpet for their annual awards evening. It's a crazy mix of GLITTER, GLAM and popping CAMERA FLASHES! Black Stripe is dressed to the nines and hoping her outfit will make the pages of L.O.L. Glam Life magazine.

2

OH BB, BB

IT'S SHOWTIME! Miss Jive begins by introducing a new character - Pops Gravy. The L.O.L.s gasp... WHO IS THIS MYSTERY GAL? When they find out it's a new L.O.L. girl band, they go wild, clapping along to the beat and cheering in their seats.

3

Next, it's time to see who has won the award for most glam L.O.L. Will it be Witchay Baby, Her Majesty, or someone else? The L.O.L.s are on the edge of their seats! "THE AWARD GOES TO... Glamour Queen" cries Miss Jive.

4

Glamour Queen rushes up to take centre stage... but trips on the steps in front of the whole audience. EVERYONE GASPS! But she styles it out with a breezy "I'm ok!", grabs the mic and makes a cool acceptance speech.

5

Next, Bhaddie storms the stage and tries to steal the limelight. WOAH, IS SHE FOR REAL? Glamour Queen quickly grabs the mic back, and the audience cheer like crazy. THAT'S WHAT THEY EXPECT FROM L.O.L. ROYALTY!

6

AND THE B.B. GOES TO...

Next, it's the Best Song Award. Shimone has everything crossed, and Sk8er Grrrl feels quietly confident, "THE AWARD GOES TO... Daring Diva!" She storms the stage. Suddenly, Miss Jive starts crying. WHAT COULD BE WRONG?

7

Daring Diva discovers that Miss Jive is sad, because the awards are almost over for another year. She takes out a tissue and dries Miss Jive's tear. "I GOT U, FAM," she tells her, and the audience break into applause.

8

BREAK THE INTERNET!

Suddenly, Miss Jive realises THIS IS THE MOMENT to make this the most successful awards night ever. "Come on everyone, LET'S TAKE A SELFIE! I couldn't do this without all of you!" All the winners join her on stage. Well done Miss Jive, you just got your first front page scoop!

ME... ALSO ME!

THE L.O.L. MEME MAKER IS OPEN FOR BUSINESS!

Memes are funny and cute pictures with words. Finish these phrases to make some funny L.O.L. memories!

THE WORDS FOR THE TOP GO HERE...

WHY STICK TO ONE COLOUR...

WHEN THERE'S SEVEN IN A RAINBOW!

I'M NOT SAYING I'M PURR - FECT, BUT...

...AND THE WORDS FOR THE BOTTOM GO HERE.

I WAS BORN TO...

©MGA

Here's a phone screen for you to draw your own meme. Make it totes Hil- L.O.L.- rious!

THERE'S NO SUCH THING AS...

LOST AND FOUND

Thrilla has dropped her phone. Which path should she take to find it?

A

B

C

ANSWER ON PAGE 76

PUMP UP THE VOLUME!

TAKE IT TO THE NEXT LEVEL WITH THIS PUFFY SLIME RECIPE!

YOU WILL NEED
113G (4 OZ) GLUE
BOWL
113G (4 OZ) WARM WATER
FOOD COLOURING
SHAVING CREAM
LIQUID LAUNDRY DETERGENT
SPOON

I'M NOT MESSY, I'M CR8TIVE.

1 Pour the glue into a bowl.

2 Mix in the warm water a little at a time.

3 Mix in a few drops of food colouring and mix thoroughly.

4 Pump in the shaving cream a bit at a time and mix thoroughly until the texture is like marshmallow cream.

5 Mix in the liquid laundry detergent a little at a time. Your slime could go hard if you mix in too much at once.

6 Knead the slime, and in seconds it should be ready to play with!

WAKE ME UP B4 YOU GOO - GOO!

RAINBOW IS MY FAVOURITE COLOUR!

ADD SOME COLOUR POPS TO THE SLIME SPLATS ON THE PAGE!

27

WHO'S REPRESENTIN'?

WE'VE PICKED OUT SOME OF OUR MOST ROCKING L.O.L. CHARACTERS. WHICH ONES DO YOU HAVE?

- ● POPULAR
- ✦ FANCY
- ★ RARE
- ♥ ULTRA-RARE

★ **Scribbles**

ART CLUB

WANT ☐ OWN ☐

✦ **Roller Sk8ter**

ATHLETIC CLUB

WANT ☐ OWN ☐

✦ **Leading Baby**

GLAM CLUB

WANT ☐ OWN ☐

✦ **Daring Diva**

POP CLUB

WANT ☐ OWN ☐

©MGA

Shorty

HIP HOP CLUB

WANT ☐ OWN ☐

Midnight

COSPLAY CLUB

WANT ☐ OWN ☐

B.B. Bop

RETRO CLUB

WANT ☐ OWN ☐

Cozy Babe

CHILL OUT CLUB

WANT ☐ OWN ☐

Hops

STORYBOOK CLUB

WANT ☐ OWN ☐

Rocker

GLEE CLUB

WANT ☐ OWN ☐

NO SIGNAL!

DISASTER! ROYAL HIGH-NEY CAN'T GET ANY PHONE RECEPTION. CAN YOU HELP HER?

PICK UP!

Which L.O.L.'s are trying to FaceTime Royal High-Ney? Draw lines to match the L.O.L. names to the correct screen.

Suite Princess

As If Baby

Black Tie

SCRAMBLED L.O.L.

Jet-Set Q.T. just sent Royal High-Ney a cute pet pic, but she dropped her phone. Disaster! Which Glam Club L.O.L. pet is this?

Dollmatian

TICK YOUR ANSWER

It Kitty

MESSAGE ME

Fill in the missing words in Royal High-Ney's texts. Use the word list below to help you.

WRITE YOUR ANSWERS ON THE LINES

WANNA MEET ME FOR A

_____

DOLL FACE, YOU ARE SO THE

_____

HEY LIL' FLOWER CHILD, DO YOU NEED A

_____

BEST   BOTTLE   SMOOTHIE

LE SIGH...

CASE CRAZY

Royal High-Ney needs a new phone case. Can you draw one for her? Make sure it's glam enough for this super-bling L.O.L.

ANSWERS ON PAGE 76 - 77

33

©MGA

WHO'S YOUR LIL' SIS SENSATION?

FIND OUT WHO YOUR PERFECT MINI MATCH WOULD BE!

THEY SEE ME STROLLIN'!

TICK ONE ANSWER FOR EACH QUESTION

1 WHAT ACCESSORY WOULD YOU CHOOSE?

Hairband

Nappy pin

Dummy

2 CHOOSE AN ACTIVITY FOR YOUR LIL' SIS

Craft

Shopping

Music

PAINT A PICTURE... IT'LL LAST LONGER.

3 WHAT KIND OF HAIRSTYLE SHOULD SHE HAVE?

Neat, and two-tone

The bigger the better

Crazy colours, and edgy too!

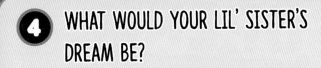

4 WHAT WOULD YOUR LIL' SISTER'S DREAM BE?

To be a famous artist

To make a show-stopping entrance in the fashion world!

To rock out on stage

5 WHICH WORD JUMPS OUT TO YOU MOST?

Creative

Glitter

Rockin'

Add up your answers to reveal your Lil' Sister match.

MOSTLY ⭐

You're super-creative, just like your Art Club match, Lil' Pop Heart. You two would have so much fun crafting, creating and conjuring up arty ideas!

MOSTLY ♥

Whoa there, you're so glam, you could out-glitz Glitterati Club queen Lil' Bling Queen!

MOSTLY ✦

Grab your guitar and go crazy with Glee Club gal Lil' Rocker. You two could put on a rockin' show, any time!

35

©MGA

SWEET 'N' SUPER SMOOTHIES

MAKE LIKE THE COSPLAY CLUB AND MIX UP THESE TASTY FRUIT TREATS

ASK A GROWN-UP FOR HELP WITH CUTTING AND MIXING DRINKS

I WANT IT ALL!

THE NEON Q.T.

YOU'LL NEED
ORANGE JUICE
SUGAR FREE LEMONADE
GRENADINE
ORANGE SLICES

Carefully cut slices of orange or other fruits of your choice ready to decorate your drinks.

Fill each glass about a third of the way up with orange juice.

Add lemonade to fill the glass, leaving a little space for the grenadine.

Pour a small amount of grenadine, very slowly, into each glass. The grenadine should sink to the bottom to form a pretty red layer.

Add a slice of orange to the side of each glass.

Serve immediately!

THE BON BON

PRETTY IN PASTEL

YOU'LL NEED

RASPBERRY SYRUP
SPARKLING WATER
CRUSHED ICE
COCKTAIL STICK
FRUIT

Add the raspberry syrup to a glass.

Slowly pour in sparkling water.

Add crushed ice.

Garnish with a cocktail stick threaded with blueberries or other fruit.

TEE HEE

THE FANIME

YOU'LL NEED

10 STRAWBERRIES
1 MANGO
LOTS OF ICE
A FEW SQUIRTS OF HONEY
A BLENDER

Blend the strawberries with ice until smooth.

Pour the mixture into a glass.

Blend the mango with the ice and honey.

Pour it on to the top of the strawberry mixture for a cool two-tone drink!

JUST CHILL!

THE CHILL OUT CLUB AND THEIR LIL' SISTERS ARE GETTING THEIR POSES ON!

Tick a pose when you've tried it!

THE SNOW ANGEL

I TRIED THIS!
YES ☐ NO ☐

THE BIG CITY STRETCH

I TRIED THIS!
YES ☐ NO ☐

THE POSH

I TRIED THIS!
YES ☐ NO ☐

©MGA

THE BABE IN THE WOODS

I TRIED THIS!
YES ☐ NO ☐

THE LIL' BRRR B.B.

I TRIED THIS!
YES ☐ NO ☐

THE COZY BABE

I TRIED THIS!
YES ☐ NO ☐

©MGA

UP ALL NIGHT!

THROW THE PYJAMA PARTY OF THE CENTURY THANKS TO THE SLEEPOVER CLUB!

MORNINGS ARE OVERRATED.

SIGN SENSATION

YOU'LL NEED
COLOURING PENCILS
SCISSORS

ZZZ
ONLY DIVAS ALLOWED!

1 Colour in this super-cute sign.

2 Carefully cut out (or photocopy) the sign along the dotted lines.

3 Hang it on your bedroom door next time you have a sleepover!

 SCISSOR WARNING!

FINISH ACTIVITIES ON PAGES 39 AND 42 BEFORE CUTTING OUT!

40

PIN THE MASK

1 Carefully cut out (or photocopy) your mask and Sleepy B.B. along the dotted lines.

2 Place sticky tack on the back of the mask.

3 Ask your friends to line up and ask the first friend to shut her eyes.

4 Give her the mask and gently spin her around three times.

5 Point her towards Sleepy BB and ask her to place the mask where she thinks it should go.

6 Mark the spot where she places the mask with her name.

7 Once everyone has had a go, the friend with the mask nearest to the correct position wins.

©MGA

THAT'S MY JAM!

WHEN SHE ROCKS THE MIC, SHE ROCKS THE MIC RIGHT!

THESE BOOTS WERE MADE FOR ROCKIN'!

SING UR HEART OUT!

Choose a line from each panel.

I ROCK THEREFORE I JAM.

I ROCK SO HARD I RIP RIGHT THROUGH PAPER.

ROCK – THAT'S HOW I ROLL.

BORN TO SPARKLE!

1 - LOL - HOTLINE - BLING

I POP TO THE TOP OF THE CHARTS.

I WAS BORN THIS WAY!

I'M BUBBLY CUZ I'M A POP SINGER.

I DROP RHYMES LIKE BABIES DROP BEDTIMES.

I SPIT RHYMES LIKE BABIES SPIT MILK.

CHECK OUT MY BEATS!

Now put your lyrics together to make your very own L.O.L. Surprise! Song. Drop the mic!

SING IT!

Can you find the totally rockin' words hidden in the wordsearch below?

Mashup Acapella Duet Rap Classical Pop Harmony Rock

```
R N U X J R B M T H D O O O C O W Y
S G D M U J A E M N U A O E O M P T
O A H C Z A S P R Z E M K C L M O G
A A W I L F W V O B T U O H W D P M
O C N S M A Q N C G N W E A T S U P
P A G A A Q S F K A F D Q R O B A H
R P Q F S A W S J F G Z M M V D K H
W E Y Y H W F N I Z S I X O O F I L
C L H S U L P W J C N J H N K E N B
J L K Q P G L P U A A D G Y T I Y L
L A V Q F C I A O G F L X L O C I N
K E B V G O B D Z L S L H J U W L C
```

ANSWERS ON PAGE 77

#NO FILTER

EVER WONDERED WHAT THE DOLLS GET UP TO BEHIND-THE-SCENES? WELL, HERE'S YOUR CHANCE!

GIRLS JUST WANNA HAVE SUN!

THE DOLLS ARE ALWAYS READY TO HOP TO IT AND GET SELFIE READY!

ALWAYS LOOKING FIERCE IS SNOW JOKE

BEING IN THE L.O.L. SURPRISE! GANG IS ROYALLY GOOD FUN!

IT'S ALL ABOUT THE CAT-TITUDE!

Draw your own L.O.L. moment here and give it a caption! Selfie game strong!

45

©MGA

PURR-ZZLES, BABY!

HELP THE PETS SOLVE THESE FUR-TASTIC PUZZLES. #PAWSOME!

BUNNY FROM THE BLOCK

HOP TO IT!

Bunny Hun wants some bunny to play with. Help her hurry through the maze to M.C. Hammy.

START

FINISH

FELINE FINE

LOOKIN' GOOD, FELINE GOOD!

Kitty Kitty is furry thirsty. Which path will lead her to a clawsome drink of milk?

milk

NAME THAT PET!

Use the first letter of your first name to find your pet-tastic name.

A KIRBY
B LOGIC
C DUNKIN
D SKIPPY
E TINY
F RASCAL
G QUICK
H IZZY
I JACQUES

J MARIO
K REX
L BULLSEYE
M TIA
N SIMBA
O CHILL
P MITTENS
Q TREAT
R POUNCE

S QUEEN
T LALA
U TREASURE
V SNUGGLES
W COTTON
X LUNA
Y SPRINKLES
Z ASTRAL

FINISHED? GIVE YOURSELF A ROUND OF APPAWS!

ANSWERS ON PAGE 77

©MGA

PAWSOME PICTURE!

GRAB THE OP-PURR-TUNITY TO BRING THIS PICTURE TO LIFE! #RAISE THE RUFF!

Use your favourite pens and pencils to make these BFFs looks fur-bulous!

WHO'S FOOLIN' WHO?

THE L.O.L. DOLLS HAVE GOT IN A MUDDLE. SPOT THE ODD ONE OUT IN EACH ROW.

ANSWERS ON PAGE 77

51

©MGA

PET PARADE!

L.O.L. SURPRISE! IS PACKED WITH FUR-BULOUS PETS. HERE'S JUST SOME OF THEM. HOW MANY DO YOU HAVE?

- ● POPULAR
- ♡ FABULOUS
- ✦ FANCY
- ★ RARE
- ♥ ULTRA-RARE

ROLLIN' 2 DA BEACH

GLYPHS OR IT DIDN'T HAPPEN!

● **Hammy Tide**

SWIM CLUB

WANT ☐ OWN ☐

✦ **Ancient Meow**

THEATRE CLUB

WANT ☐ OWN ☐

SHOOT 4 THE MOON!

SQUEAK AGAINST THE MACHINE!

✦ **Racoon-stronaut**

S.T.E.M. CLUB

WANT ☐ OWN ☐

♥ **Punk H.O.G.**

ROCK CLUB

WANT ☐ OWN ☐

Short Stop Hop
ATHLETIC CLUB
WANT ☐ OWN ☐

Brrrd
CHILL OUT CLUB
WANT ☐ OWN ☐

Midnight Pup
COSPLAY CLUB
WANT ☐ OWN ☐

The Great Ferret
GLAM CLUB
WANT ☐ OWN ☐

M.C. Hammy
GLEE CLUB
WANT ☐ OWN ☐

Splash Meow-Maid
GLITERRATI CLUB
WANT ☐ OWN ☐

©MGA

55

©MGA

Neigh Majesty

GLAM CLUB

WANT ☐ OWN ☐

Pup Bee

GLITERRATI CLUB

WANT ☐ OWN ☐

Sugar Pup

OPPOSITES CLUB

WANT ☐ OWN ☐

Fuzzy Fan

COSPLAY

WANT ☐ OWN ☐

Pup in the Woods

CHILL OUT CLUB

WANT ☐ OWN ☐

Rolls

ATHLETIC

WANT ☐ OWN ☐

COPY CAT!

TEST YOUR DRAWING SKILLS AND SEE IF YOU CAN COPY THESE FIERCE LOOKS.

Sugar always looks sweet enough to eat. Copy her outfit here.

99% angel 1% trouble!

©MGA

No one does make-up like Kawaii Queen. Try out her look here.

Fierce

Sugar Queen and Spice love their hairbands. Can you create a fierce 'n' fab one here?

BEST FRIENDS

BFF'S 4 EVA

LUV U

LOVIN' THOSE LIL' SISTERS!

ALMOST EVERY L.O.L. SURPRISE DOLL HAS A CUTE LIL' SISTER TO SWAP AND SHARE ACCESSORIES WITH.

DRIBBLE, DRIBBLE, SCORE!

Can you match each Lil' Sister to her big sis?

I'VE GOT A HEART OF GOLD.

IN IT TO WIN IT!

I'M THE BABE WITH THE POWER.

Which doll doesn't have a Lil' Sister ?

ANSWER ON PAGE 77

58

©MGA

Here are some ideas to get you started:

NEW WORLD. WHO DIS?

WHERE DID IT HAPPEN?

My BFF's house ◯   School ◯

A sleepover ◯   Home ◯

 Somewhere else ◯

....

I WAS WITH:

My class ◯

My parents ◯   My BFF ◯

 Someone else ◯

....

I FELT:

Happy ◯

Sad ◯   Excited ◯

Embarrassed ◯

 Something else ◯

....

WHAT HAPPENED?

My BFF had a fashion crisis ◯

I woke up in the L.O.L. Surprise! world ◯

I fell over in front of my whole class! ◯

 Something else ◯

....

....

....

ROCK OUT!

TICK THE ANSWERS THAT BEST DESCRIBE YOU, THEN COUNT UP WHICH LETTER YOU PICKED THE MOST TO REVEAL WHICH INSTRUMENT YOU SHOULD PLAY.

WHAT'S THE FIRST THING YOU DO IN THE MORNING?

A Shower.
B Stretch.
C Smile.

WHERE WOULD YOU LOVE TO LIVE?

A Why would I want to live anywhere else than here?
B Somewhere hot and laid-back.
C New York. It's always on the go like me.

WHAT'S YOUR BEST QUALITY?

A I'm a good listener.
B My passion, baby.
C My sense of humour.

THAT'S SO FUNKADELIC!

COLOUR IN FUNKY Q.T. AND GRUNGE GRRRL SO THEY CAN ROCK OUT IN STYLE!

WHAT'S YOUR BIGGEST FLAW? BE HONEST ;)

A I can get carried away.
B I can fly off the handle!
C I can't sit still.

LET'S RIOT!

BORN TO BE BAD!

WHAT'S YOUR FAVE ITEM IN YOUR WARDROBE?

A My unicorn onesie.

B My comfiest jeans and trusty trainers.

C Whatever's the most fashion-forward.

WHAT PART WOULD YOU PREFER IN THE SCHOOL PLAY?

A A small part would suit me.

B I'd love to be involved in creating the scenery.

C Centre stage of course, darling!

BORN TO BE BAD!

MOSTLY A'S
You should pick up the saxophone.

You're not looking for anything fancy or cutting-edge, you just need to play something which you can truly jam on. The saxophone's sultry tones will speak to your soul.

MOSTLY B'S
You should pick up the violin.

You're the strong, silent type, but when you do express yourself, you don't hold back. That kind of focused passion is perfect for the violin.

MOSTLY C'S
You should pick up the banjo.

Your energy and love for life are undeniable and you need an instrument that can keep up with your fast-moving fingers. The pay-off will be twangy amazingness.

©MGA

TIME TO WARM UP!

THE TOTS ARE OUT IN THE FREEZING SNOW. RACE THROUGH THE GAME TO SEE WHO GETS TO WARM THEMSELVES UP WITH A BRRR...ILLIANT HOT CHOC FIRST!

Start

1

2

3

4
IT'S SLIPPERY! MOVE ON TWO SPACES.

5

6

7
PUP IN THE WOODS HAS FALLEN OVER. YOU STOP TO HELP. MISS A TURN.

8

9
YOU STOP TO BUILD A SNOWMAN WITH COZY KITTY. MISS A TURN.

10

11

18

1

YOU'LL NEED
SCISSORS
GLUE

1 Carefully cut out the dice and counters along the bold black lines.

2 Fold along the dotted lines.

3 Glue down the tabs to make the dice.

IF YOU DON'T WANT TO RUIN YOUR ANNUAL, TRACE OR PHOTOCOPY THE DICE AND COUNTERS AND CAREFULLY CUT OUT.

2 13

14
BIG CITY B. B. HANDS YOU A HUGE SCARF SO YOU CAN PLAY LONGER.
TAKE ANOTHER TURN.

15

16
OH NO! SNOW GETS INTO YOUR BOOTS. YOU HAVE TO GO HOME AND CHANGE.
GO BACK TO THE START!

7

1 3 2 4 5 6

20
Finish
WELL DONE! GO MAKE YOURSELF A DELICIOUS HOT CHOCOLATE.

FINISH ACTIVITY ON PAGE 66 BEFORE CUTTING OUT!

©MGA

FRESH BEATS!

IT'S TIME TO WORK IT!

WORK IT B.B!

D.J. knows that music is an awesome way to feel great. What songs would make your Fresh Beats playlist? Fill in the cassette labels.

A SONG THAT MAKES YOU SMILE.

A SONG THAT MAKES YOU WANNA GET UP AND DANCE.

A SONG THAT REMINDS YOU OF AN AWESOME TIME.

YOU AND YOUR BFF'S SONG.

A SONG THAT MAKES YOU WANNA SING ALONG AT THE TOP OF YOUR VOICE.

FREE STYLIN' DOODLES ♪

CRAZY SLEEPY COOL!

Play Beats' doodle game with a friend. Take it in turns to think of a song lyric, then draw it in three doodles. Have fun guessing the lyrics!

GUESS THE LYRICS HERE:

REVEAL THE LYRICS HERE:

GUESS THE LYRICS HERE:

REVEAL THE LYRICS HERE:

PIZZA PARTY!

BABY NEXT DOOR HAS SETTLED INTO THE L.O.L. SURPRISE HOUSE AND IS THROWING A PIZZA PARTY TO CELEBRATE!

Baby Next Door is hosting an epic pizza party for all her BFFs. THE L.O.L. SURPRISE HOUSE IS ROCKING. Everyone's having the most fabulous time.

Even Little Baby Next Door wants to stay up, but Baby Next Door tells her to go to bed. IT'S NOT ALWAYS FUN BEING A BABY.

Just then, As If Baby spots Baby Next Door. SHE GASPS IN HORROR as she takes in Baby Next Door's laid-back playsuit and tee.

"WHAT ARE YOU WEARING?" As If Baby asks, her mouth hanging open. "Clothes?" shrugs Baby Next Door holding out a slice of pizza.

5

As If Baby shakes her head in despair. THIS IS NO TIME FOR PIZZA! Baby Next Door is dressed way too casually to party! Something needs to be done right now.

6

As If Baby's eyes light up. "YOU NEED A PARTY OUTFIT!" she grins. She glitterally can't wait to give Baby Next Door a makeover.

7

THERE'S NO TIME TO WASTE. As If Baby runs to her wardrobe and starts throwing potential outfits at Baby Next Door. The floor is soon covered with party dresses.

8

Baby Next Door spots a red, glittery top and skirt. It's the perfect outfit. "YAAS!" shouts As If Baby. Baby Next Door grabs it and runs off to change.

9

EVERYONE GOES WILD as Baby Next Door sashays into the party, looking like a million dollars. "Thanks so much!" Baby Next Door smiles happily at As If Baby.

10

Suddenly Baby Next Door trips over her own feet. For a moment, everyone holds their breath, but she just giggles. IT'S TIME FOR PIZZA, DANCING AND FUN! YASS!

CODE-CRACKING!

SHHH! V.R.Q.T. HAS LEFT A TOP SECRET MESSAGE FOR YOU. ALL YOU HAVE TO DO IS CUT IT OUT, FOLD IT LIKE A FAN AND THE MESSAGE WILL BE REVEALED.

WHAT'S THE WIFI PASSWORD?

1 Carefully cut out (or photocopy) the pattern on the opposite page along the dashed lines.

2 Now fold like a fan. Fold the top of the paper towards you up to the first row of shapes, the red lines show where the folds should be.

3 Flip over and fold exactly back on itself.

4 Repeat this folding pattern until you reach the bottom of the paper.

5 Now stretch out the fan and hold it up horizontally with the bottom facing you.

6 You should see a secret message!

70

ANSWER ON PAGE 77

©MGA

FINISH ACTIVITY ON PAGE 72 BEFORE CUTTING OUT!

TOP

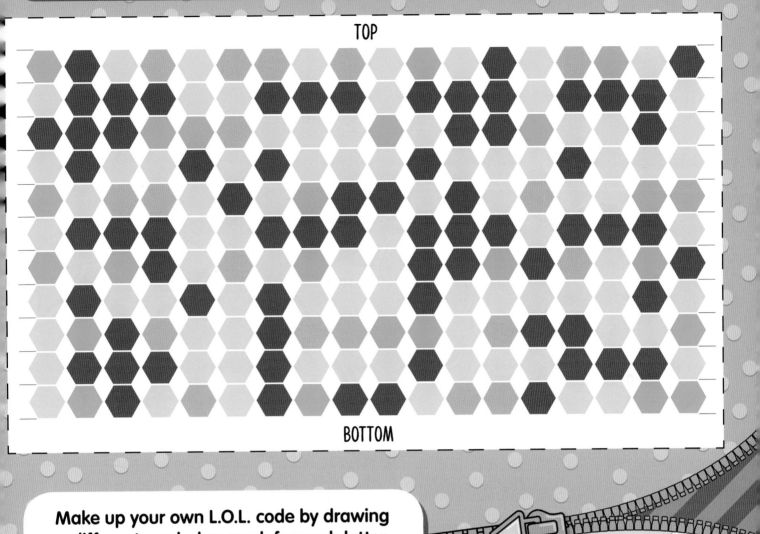

BOTTOM

Make up your own L.O.L. code by drawing a different symbol or mark for each letter. Share it with your BFF and use it every time you need to pass on a top-secret message.

A
B
C
D
E
F

G
H
I
J
K
L

M
N
O
P
Q
R
S

T
U
V
W
X
Y
Z

OH SO DIFFERENT!

THERE'S NO TIME TO NAP, FIND THE FIVE DIFFERENCES BETWEEN THESE TWO BABIES PICTURES!

PICTURE A

Circle the differences in picture B.

PICTURE B

ANSWERS ON PAGE 77

©MGA

QUIZ TIME

These dolls may all have completely different looks, but there's one thing they've all so got in common! Name the five dolls pictured here, then use the missing letters to find out what it is.

___HEEKY BABE

CHEEKY ___EDGEHOG

D___VA

RO___KER

WRITE YOUR ANSWER HERE:

___ ___ ___ ___ ___

GLITTER ON!

One of these Boss Queens isn't looking quite so like a boss! Can you spot which one is different?

TROPHY CABINET!

HERE'S AN AWARDS CABINET WITH A DIFFERENCE.

Decorate these trophies then have fun creating your own.

Short Stop Hop

Short Stop

DESIGN YOUR OWN AWARDS HERE! GO BLING-TASTIC!

Pup in the Woods

Choose from the nominated dolls on these pages or choose your own dolls to win the awards!

THE AWARD FOR THE
Most Pawsome Pet
GOES TO

....

Super B.B.

Pop Heart

Babe in the Woods

Center Stage

#Instagold

THE AWARD FOR THE
Blingiest Baby
GOES TO

....

Bon Bon

Hop Hop

Lil Purple Queen

Dollface

THE AWARD FOR THE
Best L.O.L. Doll of All Time
GOES TO

....

Purple Queen

Lil Dollface

Neon Kitty

Hoops D.O.G.G.

Hoops MVP

Neon Q.T.

75

©MGA

PUZZLE ANSWERS

PAGE 6

BRING THE BLING!

START

FINISH

PAGE 8

GOOD BOY!
Kitty Queen - Kitty Kitty.

TREAT TIME
Rocker - Ruff Rocker.

FETCH!
Black Tie - Black Stripe.

PAGES 10-11

CHILLS AND THRILLS

YOU'VE BEEN PRANKED!

Snow Angel   Cozy Babe   Snow Bunny

PAGE 12-13

WORD UP

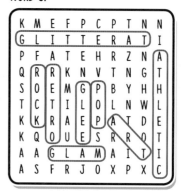

The missing club is Cosplay.

SOOO CREATIVE

The missing name is Eau De Splatters.

THE A TEAM
Hoops, Kicks, Touchdown and Spike made the team.

PAGE 25

LOST AND FOUND
Path B leads to Thrilla's phone.

PAGES 32-33

PICK UP!

Suite Princess   As If Baby   Black Tie

PAGES 32-33 continued

SCRAMBLED L.O.L.
Dollmation.

MESSAGE ME
Wanna meet me for a smoothie.
Doll Face, you are SO the best.
Hey Lil' Flower Child, do you need a bottle?

PAGE 42

SING IT!

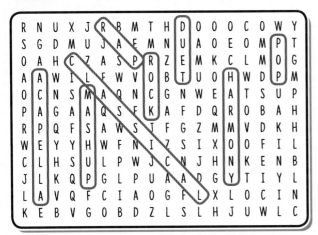

PAGE 48

HOP TO IT!

FELINE FINE
Path C leads to the milk.

PAGE 51

WHO'S FOOLIN' WHO

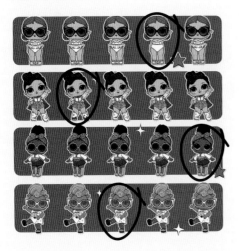

PAGE 58-59

LOVIN' THOSE LIL SISTERS!
Bon Bon doesn't have a Lil Sister.

#GLAMLIFE

PAGE 70-71

CODE-CRACKING
The secret message is BFFS

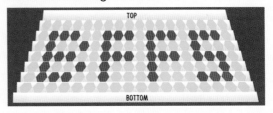

PAGES 72-73

OH SO DIFFERENT

QUIZ TIME
The dolls are all chic.

GLITTER ON!